My Unique Family & Me

By: Atiya Lynnette Butler · Illustrated by: Linda Kuo

To my potato, inspiration & motivation: Donovan

Hi! My name is Rachel. In my house it is just me and my dad. We are a very small family and that is what makes us unique.

I love my dad and he loves me!

I'm Troy! In my family my mommy is a Sailor and my daddy is a Soldier. Sometimes when they're away, my grandparents come to take care of my sister and me. My family changes often, and that's what makes us unique.

I love Mommy, Daddy, Gigi, Papa, and Tzipporah ! And they love me!

Hello, I am Kristine. My daddy has four daughters, and my step-mommy has three sons! We have a blended family, and that's what makes us unique.

I love my daddy, my step-mommy, Sarah, Simone, Sheryl, Jonathan, James, and George! And they love me!

Hi, I am Lizzy! I have two awesome mommies and a cat, Gorda! I call one Mater and I call the other Mommy, and that's what makes us unique.

I love Mater, Mommy, and Gorda la Gata. And they love me!

Hello there! My name is Joshua! In my family, my brother was born unable to see , which means he is blind. Dad, Mom, and I work as a team to help care for his needs, and this is what makes my family unique.

I love Aiden, my mom, and my dad. And they love me!

Hey, it's me, Penelope! In my family, Daddy is brown, Mama is tan, my sisters are also very brown like Daddy, but I am very pale because I have albinism. I look very different from my siblings, and that is what makes my family unique.

I love Mama, Daddy, Lillian, and Krista. And they love me!

Hi, I am Aminah. My family are expats who moved for new discoveries and opportunities. Sometimes I have to help translate for my family since everything is so new, and that's what makes us unique.

I love my Ummi, my Abu, and Ishmael. And they love me!

Hi! I am Kelsey! I was adopted by my family when I was just five years old. I was an addition to an original family of four. They treat me just like family, and that is what makes us unique.

I love my new mom, my dad, Candice, Adam, and my new dog, Pogo. And they love me!

Hola! Me llamo Miquel! In my family, my mother is from the Philippines, and my dad is from Puerto Rico. Our blended cultures make family dinners special, with meals like pancit and empañadas. This is what makes my family unique!

I love Tatay and Mamá. And they love me!

Hey! My name is Vanessa, and I came as a surprise!
My first older sibling is fourteen years older than
me! It is awesome having such older siblings, and
this is what makes us unique.

I love my cool dad, my mommy, Andrew, and Kourtney! And they love me!

No matter how big or small. Whether it is blended or single. It can be eccentric or conservative. Even foreign or local.

Everyone's family is unique! And all that matters is that they love YOU!